I dedicate this book to my oldest brother, **David Bon Kartelli**, who always told me to believe in myself and my capabilities.

Thank you, David, for always loving and guiding me. I love and miss you so much.

This is for you!

Riah's Way

presents

Beauty Begins in Me

written by Mariah Cubano
illustrated by Subi Bosa

ISBN: 978-0-578-94821-8
Copyright 2021 Mariah Cubano

I've been told

beauty begins in me.

I am much more than what you see.

My beauty is
deep down
inside me.

I've been taught by my parents that

beauty is shown, not seen,
and this is what I mean.

Beauty is how you speak,
think, and act.

In fact, they've even given me,

"A Beauty Recipe!"

I've been told to share this recipe with all those listening.

The first ingredient is:
Affirmations.

Affirmations remind you of how **powerful** and **special** you are.

Step 1:

Sprinkle 1/3 cup of **affirmations** into your daily routine.

Proudly walk over to the mirror,
something I do with my little brother,

And say,

"I am confident."

"I am kind."

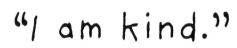

"I am brave."

"I can do anything!"

Be sure, when you say this,
you speak clear, **loud,** and **PROUD.**

The second ingredient is:
Compliments.

Compliments remind other people
how **appreciated**
and **special** they are.

Step 2:

Sprinkle 1/3 cup of Compliments into your daily routine

by proudly walking
over to someone,

and saying,

"You are kind."

"You are brave."

"You can do anything!"

Be sure when you say this,
you are **genuine** and **sincere**.

The third ingredient
in the "Beauty Recipe" is:
Positivity.

Positivity is how you act
in every situation.

Be sure to never be **rude** or **mean**.

Step 3:

Sprinkle
1/3 cup of **Positivity** into your daily
routine by always doing your best
to see the bright side of things,

even when they **don't** go your way.

Step 4:

Mix affirmations,
compliments, and positivity,

and voila, there you have it,

You are BEAUTIFUL!

Be sure to add **ALL** three ingredients **everyday,**

and you will be
full of **beauty!!**

Now that you know the
"Beauty Recipe,"

please share it with a friend
as I shared it with you.

So we can all

BE BEAUTIFUL!

CPSIA information can be obtained
at www.ICGtesting.com
Printed in the USA
BVHW021445190821
614781BV00005BA/12